Worrywart Willow

by Emily McHugh

Illustrated by Mary Elizabeth Dickman

First and foremost, to my father who told me more than I can count, while growing up, that I should be a children's author. I will never stop missing you and trying to make you proud. To my mom who gives endless amounts of support with everything I do in my life. Tristan, thank you for always encouraging me to achieve my goals. Maura, Keelin, and Callum, thank you for being the loves of my life and inspiring me every day. Love you to the end of the universe and back! Thank you to the family and friends in my little circle who are always there for me and have been excited for me since day one about my first book! You know who you are. Love you all! Finally, to Finn, who was always by my side, especially as I began this story. Every single day, you were my "calm down spot", and I will never stop wishing I had more time with you. ~XO

— EM

To my husband, Andrew; my children, Eric and Emily; and our fur child, Cody, who will forever be in our hearts. Thank you, as well, to all of my family and friends.

— MED

"Notice that the stiffest tree is most easily cracked, while the bamboo or willow survives by bending with the wind."

— Bruce Lee

In my backyard, next to a stream, there's a Willow Tree and she's my tree. Well, I didn't actually plant her, but when my mom and dad moved into our house, I was in my mom's belly. My mom said she loved our house because she loved that tree.

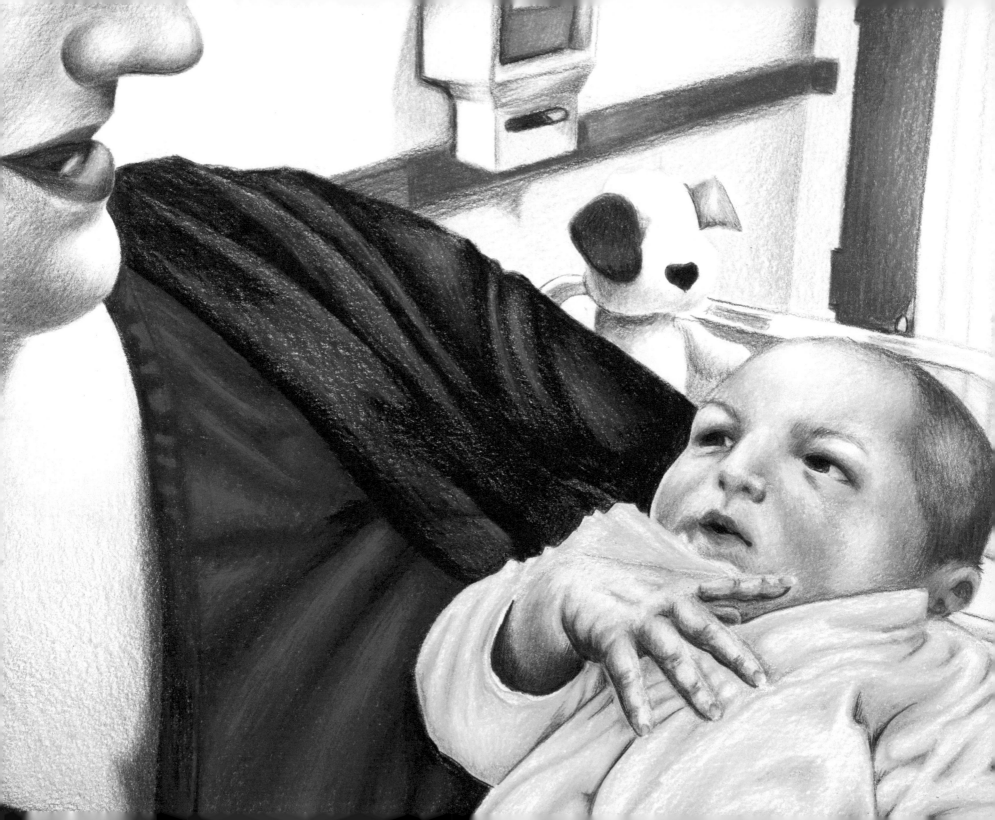

One time, I asked my mom why she loved that tree so much and she told me she admired them since Willows are very strong and can survive no matter what storms come at her.

She must have **really** loved willow trees because when I was born, she named me Willow.

My full name is Willow Leigh Delaney, but my older sister sometimes calls me "Worrywart Willow."

My sister Alice is in the fourth grade. She can be cool and let me play with her and her friends, but she sometimes likes to pick on me.

"Stop being such a Worrywart Willow," she likes to say.

She calls me that when I get a bellyache about going upstairs by myself…

Or when I have to speak to someone I don't know…

Sometimes, she calls me that when I tell her about being afraid at night or when I ask her "what if" questions…

"What if all of this raining makes it flood??"

"Or what if that lightning strikes our house??"

"What if Mom and Dad get lost and don't come back from their date??"

"What if I get sick at school??"

"You're being a worrywart, Worrywart Willow," Alice replies.

One day, I was out front, trying on my new rollerblades I had just gotten for my birthday. My friends were all out playing, too. Normally, I love playing with my friends, but since I was practicing my skating skills, I had a funny feeling in my belly about them watching.

I was doing such an amazing job when things turned from fun to bad.

I was zooming up and down the driveway, feeling like the best skater ever when the ball my sister and her friends were playing with came straight for my feet.

I tried to move to the side, but my legs didn't want to. I tried to stop but my skates didn't want to. I hit the ball hard and went flying.

Luckily, something broke my fall: our garbage can.

I dove up into the air and came down hard. I finally stopped next to the container on a few bags of garbage.

I laid there for a minute, waiting to see if I had broken a leg, my arm, or my head, when I heard the giggling.

I looked up from the garbage and saw some of the kids from the neighborhood laughing at me. Alice looked like she was going to join in but then had a sad face. I didn't want them to see me cry, so I ripped my skates off and ran back to the house.

I yelled for my mom but she wasn't there. That made me cry harder. I felt a hand on my shoulder and was happy to finally have my mom there, but I turned to find my sister instead.

"Are you okay, Worryw…are you hurt, Willow?" she asked.

I looked down and was surprised to not find any blood or bruises. I really wasn't hurt but my feelings were.

Alice told me that our mom was at the backyard weeding and said she'd go out with me to find her.

Mom was down by the willow tree and I ran to her as fast as I could in my bare feet. I grabbed her around her waist and snuggled my face into her belly. She dried my tears and I told her the embarrassing garbage story.

"That must have been scary and humiliating," she told me. "When I was a little girl, I sometimes had worries like you. Grandma had me go to a spot that was all mine where I could calm down and try to feel better.

What if we found a place for you like that? Maybe something outside because nature always has a way of soothing us."

I thought for a minute about where I could go. My room? No, I didn't want to go up there alone. The basement? Definitely no. As I thought, I looked over to the big Willow.

Her long swaying branches looked like arms that would hug me if I was sad. I got a big smile on my face and went over. One of her branches was low to the ground and looked like a seat. This would be perfect for me, I told my mom. As I felt the wind blow my hair back and her leaves tickling my face, I started to feel better. I think my mom was right about nature taking our worries away!

"Willow trees are strong, just like you," Mom told me. "When you worry, you're still a strong girl but you have to tell the part of your brain that worries to go away because you're bigger than those fears."

So, when my second-grade teacher had us write about our favorite spot that our parents didn't have to drive us to, I knew right away what I'd pick.

She's my tree because my mom and dad call her my "calm down spot." When I'm sad or angry with my sister, I can go sit under her leaves and no one can see me. Sometimes, I take my sketchbook to color, my belly in the soft grass, and she watches me create my artwork.

I start to feel so much better as I take a deep breath and hear her branches dance all around me in the wind.

Maybe when I'm older, I'll still be a worrywart sometimes, but I'll always be strong...

Just like my willow tree.

Since she was a young child, Emily McHugh loved to come up with stories and write creatively. Her father was always telling her she should publish a book and encouraging her to do so. She graduated with a degree in English Education and enjoyed teaching reading and writing to middle school students. After the birth of her first daughter, she took time off from teaching, and to help her stay sane from the demands of a newborn, she began writing a blog, "The Sweet and Sour Mom." This hobby as a blogger became a passion and Emily was soon publishing on other sites and growing a following on social media. Worrywart Willow is her first children's book, and although her dad, who lost his battle with cancer in 2019, did not get to read it, she knows he's happy she finally listened to him! She lives in northern Baltimore, Maryland with her husband, three kids, and a sweet, hyper pit bull mix, Fiona. When she's not writing, or being a chauffeur for her children, Emily is usually spending time outdoors hiking, running, or simply finding a peaceful spot and meditating. Having mindfulness is crucial to her happiness and something she's always trying to model for her children. You can follow her at www.emilymchughwriter.com.

Ever since drawing all over the walls, and her younger sister, with her mother's lipstick as a six-year-old, Mary Elizabeth Dickman, or Mary Beth, as she is known by her family and friends, has been cultivating and developing her artistic career. Her studies began in a private studio under the watchful eye of Bernadette Shephard, a teacher who would become a huge influence for Mary Beth. Miss Bernie's artistic passion inspired Mary Beth to pursue art for the rest of her academic and professional career. After earning her Bachelor of Arts degree from Notre Dame of Maryland University, Mary Beth earned her master's degree in art education from Towson University and found a calling in inspiring others to pursue their own artistic dreams. She is a lifelong educator and continues to share her work with the world through YouTube and Instagram under the name artbymb. Mary Beth is constantly creating art in her home studio in Baltimore, Maryland, where she lives with her husband and two children.

Printed in the USA
CPSIA information can be obtained
at www.ICGtesting.com
LVHW070721100923

757647LV00064B/353